Gone wit.. ...

Part 1

MARGARET MITCHELL

Level 4

Retold by John Escott
Series Editors: Andy Hopkins and Jocelyn Potter

2

Pearson Education Limited
Edinburgh Gate, Harlow,
Essex CM20 2JE, England
and Associated Companies throughout the world.

ISBN: 978-1-4058-8220-0

Copyright © Margaret Mitchell 1936
First published in Great Britain by Macmillan London Ltd 1936
This adaptation first published by Penguin Books 1995
Published by Addison Wesley Longman Limited and Penguin Books Ltd 1998
New edition first published 1999
This edition first published 2008

3 5 7 9 10 8 6 4 2

Text copyright © John Escott 1995
Illustrations copyright © David Cuzik 1995
All rights reserved

The moral right of the adapter and of the illustrator has been asserted

Typeset by Graphicraft Ltd, Hong Kong
Set in 11/14pt Bembo
Printed in China
SWTC/02

Published by Pearson Education Ltd in association with
Penguin Books Ltd, both companies being subsidiaries of Pearson Plc

For a complete list of the titles available in the Penguin Readers series please write to your local
Pearson Longman office or to: Penguin Readers Marketing Department, Pearson Education,
Edinburgh Gate, Harlow, Essex CM20 2JE, England.

A71368

Contents

Introduction

'You, Miss, are no lady,' Rhett Butler said. 'But ladies rarely interest me, and I cannot understand, my dear Miss O'Hara, what a wild and hot-blooded girl like you can find to like about the handsome but very boring Mr Wilkes.'

The story of *Gone with the Wind* begins in April 1861 in the southern part of the United States. Every young man for miles around is in love with sixteen-year-old Scarlett O'Hara. But Scarlett can think of no one but Ashley Wilkes, the handsome, intelligent, perfect Southern gentleman. He is planning to marry Melanie Hamilton, but Scarlett will do anything to make him love her.

But although Ashley loves Scarlett, he knows that they are wrong for each other. They are just too different. As Scarlett's father tells her, the Wilkes family 'enjoy reading books, going to Boston and New York to see paintings and hear music.' Scarlett, on the other hand, is 'a wild and hot-blooded girl', in the words of Captain Rhett Butler.

Rhett, an older man with a dark past, likes the fire in Scarlett's character and is amused by her selfishness. He is nothing like the gentlemanly Ashley, but he is clever, handsome and charming. He understands Scarlett and wants her for himself.

But as the winds of war begin to blow, Scarlett learns that, even for her, there are more important things than the admiration of men. Scarlett has to use all her cleverness and strength to stay alive.

Scarlett is a very confident, selfish young woman. She will do anything to get what she wants. But she is not completely without feelings for others. And neither is Rhett. In fact, although they fight almost every time they meet, Scarlett and

Rhett find that they have more similarities than differences in their characters.

The story of Scarlett O'Hara, Ashley Wilkes and Rhett Butler is one of the greatest love stories ever told. It is also a story of the American Civil War and the death of the lifestyle of the 'Old South' after that terrible war. That is the meaning of the title: the war sweeps through the southern state of Georgia like a wind destroying everything in its path. After the war, the Old South has 'gone with the wind'.

Before the war, Georgia and the other southern states of the US were very different from the northern states. In the north, great cities were growing up, there were many factories, and the economy was moving towards the modern age. In the south, there were very few factories. Cotton was grown in the hot southern climate and was very important for the southern economy. Most people's lifestyles still centred on farms and big cotton plantations. Southern society was old-fashioned. It was important to be a gentleman or a lady, and a man should ride and shoot well. Black slaves were still used for the hot work in the cotton fields and in people's homes.

Gone with the Wind shows us a romantic view of life in the Old South. We see it through the comfortable life of rich plantation owners who are good to their slaves.

Margaret Mitchell was born in Atlanta, Georgia on 8 November 1900. As a child, she enjoyed writing and telling stories at an early age. Like Scarlett O'Hara, Margaret enjoyed being the centre of attention. She loved parties and flirting with boys of her age. In 1918, Clifford Henry, a soldier, asked Margaret to marry him. They were planning their wedding when he was killed in battle. It was a terrible blow for Margaret.

Mrs Mitchell took her daughter to Massachusetts, where

Margaret went to Smith College. It was the last time Margaret saw her mother, who soon after became ill and died in January 1919. Margaret decided to leave college and stay at home to look after her father.

Her first marriage, in 1922, was a very unhappy one and did not last. Her husband was in some ways like Rhett Butler, and some people think that she was thinking of him when she wrote her book in later years.

Margaret went to work as a writer for the *Atlanta Journal Sunday Magazine* and continued in that job for four years. In July 1925, she married John Marsh, a friend of her first husband. After she broke a bone in her lower leg in 1926, John made a suggestion to her: he thought she should spend her time writing a book. She did, and the result was *Gone with the Wind*. It took her ten years to finish it, and she did not think it was very good. She did not want to show it to anybody at first. But when it finally appeared, so many people wanted to meet her that she had to hide!

Gone with the Wind was the only book Margaret Mitchell wrote. When she died on 16 August 1949, killed by a speeding taxi, the people of Atlanta lost a valuable member of their city. Margaret's generous work helping the sick had made her a much loved citizen. She gave so much to her city and did much good during the years of World War II. Today there is a special building in Atlanta to celebrate Margaret Mitchell's life.

The Civil War background of the story is one that she knew well from the stories of old family members. Her grandmother, for example, was the daughter of a plantation owner and remembered the life of the Old South well. They also remembered well the terrible four-year civil war in which nearly a million Americans died.

The American Civil War (1861–65) started mainly because

the thirteen southern states did not want to stay in the United States after Abraham Lincoln became president. They wanted to become a separate country from the northern states. These thirteen states were Virginia, North Carolina, South Carolina, Georgia, Tennessee, Arkansas, Texas, Louisiana, Mississippi, Alabama, Florida, Missouri and Kentucky. The US government in the north wanted to change the south and free all slaves. The south did not want the 'Yankees' in the north to tell them what to do. So these states left the United States in 1861 and called themselves the Confederate States of America, or the Confederacy.

When the Civil War began, the Confederates believed they would win: the men of the south knew how to ride and shoot better than the Yankee city boys. But the population of the southern states was only 9 million while the north's was 22 million. And, as Rhett Butler knew from the start, there were no factories in the south for making guns, and the south had no fighting ships. At first, things went well for the South. The Confederate General Robert E. Lee took some northern cities. But the Battle of Gettysburg, July 1–3 1863, changed the South's dreams. It was a very bloody battle and it ended General Robert E. Lee's successes. General Meade's northern soldiers won after taking the railway lines, weakening Lee's control. Between 46,000 and 51,000 men lost their lives in that three-day battle. But the fight was not over. Lee's army escaped into Virginia. Then the battle in Vicksburg destroyed the South's chances of ever winning.

In November 1863, President Abraham Lincoln spoke in Gettysburg and gave new meaning to the fight. It was no longer a fight to keep all of the states together, but it was a fight to make people free. It became a fight to free the slaves.

The North had the advantage of experience with sea battles and the South did not. The North blockaded the South's port cities so that nothing could get in or out. Men like Rhett Butler tried to get ships through the blockade at night. They were known as 'blockade runners'. These blockade runners were very successful at first. They could sell the south's cotton and bring in necessary things like food, medicine and guns. But this was not enough to save the Confederacy. The Yankees marched through Georgia. They burned everything in their path and they attacked the capital, Atlanta.

Like the women in Mitchell's story, Atlanta's richer women worked as nurses for the soldiers hurt in the war. Public buildings, homes, churches and streets became hospitals. Women also collected money to help the Confederate army. They sold things to get money. They collected clothes, medicine and food for the soldiers, too.

When the South finally lost the war, Atlanta's population was reduced from around 10,000 to only about 3,000.

Gone with the Wind reached the bookshops in 1936 and sold over a million copies in its first six months. It won the famous Pulitzer Prize, and then became even more famous as a film in 1939. The book is now one of the world's best sellers stories of all time.

The 1939 film by David Selznick had some of the biggest film stars of the day including Clark Gable as Rhett Butler, Vivien Leigh as Scarlett O'Hara, Leslie Howard as Ashley Wilkes and Olivia de Havilland as Melanie. It ran for three hours and thirty-nine minutes. It is probably one of the most watched films ever, and people love it today as much as they did in 1939.

Chapter 1   News of a Wedding

Scarlett O'Hara was not beautiful, but men did not realize this when caught by her charm as the Tarleton twins were. Her eyes were green, and her skin was that soft white skin which Southern women valued so highly, and covered so carefully from the hot Georgia sun with hats and gloves.

On that bright April afternoon of 1861, sixteen-year-old Scarlett sat in the cool shadows of the house at Tara, her father's plantation. Stuart and Brent Tarleton sat each side of her. They were friendly young men with deep red-brown hair, and were clever in the things that mattered in north Georgia at that time – growing good cotton, riding well, shooting straight and behaving like a gentleman.

'Don't you two care about being sent home from the University of Georgia for bad behaviour?' Scarlett was saying.

'The war* will start soon,' said Brent. 'You didn't think we'd stay in university with a war going on, did you?'

'There isn't going to be a war,' said Scarlett, looking bored. 'Ashley Wilkes and his father told Pa just last week that our men in Washington will come to an agreement with Mr Lincoln about the Confederacy.† Anyway, the Yankees‡ are too frightened of us to fight. And if you say "war" once more, I'll go inside the house and shut the door!'

They looked across the red earth of Gerald O'Hara's land, which stretched away as far as the eye could see. The white

---

* war: in this story, the word describes the American Civil War.
† Confederacy: the Southern States of America.
‡ Yankees: the name used for the soldiers and people of the Northern States of America.

house was like an island, sitting in a wild red sea, the earth blood-coloured after the rains of recent weeks.

'Scarlett, you'll promise to dance with us at the party at Twelve Oaks tomorrow, won't you?' said Brent.

'If you do, we'll tell you a secret,' said Stuart.

'What secret?' asked Scarlett. 'Who told you?'

'Miss Pittypat Hamilton, Ashley Wilkes' cousin who lives in Atlanta. Charles and Melanie Hamilton's aunt,' said Stuart.

'She said that we'll hear news of a wedding tomorrow night, at the party,' said Brent.

'Oh, I know that!' said Scarlett, disappointed. 'It's about Charlie Hamilton and Honey Wilkes. Everyone knows they'll get married some day.'

'No, it's about Ashley,' said Stuart. 'He's going to marry Charlie's sister, Miss Melanie!'

Scarlett's face did not change but her lips went white – like a person who is in the first moments of shock.

'They weren't going to marry until next year,' said Stuart, 'but with all the talk of war, both families think it will be better if they're married soon.' He smiled. 'Now, Scarlett, you must promise to eat supper with us at the party.'

'Of course I will,' said Scarlett automatically.

'And give us plenty of dances?'

'Yes.' She spoke as if in a dream.

'And sit with us at lunch, too?' said Brent.

'What?' said Scarlett. 'Oh, yes, of course.'

The twins were unable to believe their good luck. They talked on about the dance, and Ashley Wilkes and Melanie Hamilton. They laughed and joked, and waited for Scarlett to invite them to supper; and it was some time before they realized she was not listening to them.

♦

The twins waited for Scarlett to invite them to supper; and it was some time before they realized she was not listening to them.

Scarlett watched the twins ride away.

Ashley was going to marry Melanie Hamilton! Oh, it couldn't be true! It was all a mistake. Ashley was in love with *her*, not Melanie!

Mammy came out of the house. She was a big old negro who loved Ellen O'Hara and her family. 'Are the gen'lemen gone?' she asked. 'Why didn' you ask them to stay to supper?'

'I didn't want to listen to them talking to Pa about the war all through supper,' said Scarlett.

'You just ain't* polite, Miss Scarlett,' said Mammy. 'Now come into the house before you get cold.'

'I want to watch the sun go down,' said Scarlett. 'I'll sit here until Pa comes home. Just fetch me a light coat, Mammy.'

Mammy went back into the house and Scarlett made a sudden decision. 'I'll go and meet Pa,' she thought. 'He'll be coming back from Twelve Oaks soon, and he'll know about Ashley.'

As a child, Scarlett had not given Ashley Wilkes a single thought. But two years ago, he had arrived home after touring Europe – riding up to Tara with the sun so bright on his fair hair that it shone like silver. 'You've grown up, Scarlett,' he had said, kissing her hand. And from that moment on, she wanted him as simply as she wanted food to eat, and horses to ride, and a soft bed to sleep in.

For two years, he took her to dances and suppers, and a week did not go past without Ashley calling at Tara. It was true he never spoke to her of love, and his clear grey eyes never burned with that hot light Scarlett knew so well in other men. But she was sure that he loved her. She saw him looking at her some-times, in that sad, strange way of his.

Scarlett heard the sound of Gerald O'Hara's horse and saw him coming across the fields at full speed. Gerald was sixty years

* *ain't*: *aren't* or *isn't* or *haven't* in Southern American English.

4

old, a small man with silver-white hair and hard little blue eyes. He was surprised to see her.

'How is everyone at Twelve Oaks?' she asked him.

'They're all talking about the war,' he said, 'and —'

'Did they speak about the party?' Scarlett asked quickly.

'Yes, I think they did,' said Gerald. 'Miss Melanie Hamilton and her brother Charles have come from Atlanta and —'

'Oh, so she did come!' Scarlett's heart became heavy. 'Was Ashley there, too?'

'Yes, he was.' Gerald looked closely at his daughter. 'That's why you came to meet me, isn't it? Why didn't you say so before? Now what's all this about you and Ashley?'

'There's nothing, Pa,' she said.

'Has he asked to marry you?'

'No,' said Scarlett, quietly.

'And he won't,' said Gerald. 'John Wilkes says that Ashley is to marry Miss Melanie. They'll tell everyone tomorrow.'

A pain cut across Scarlett's heart and she found it hard to breathe. Her father watched her, and looked uncomfortable.

'Have you run after a man who's not in love with you?'

'No!' said Scarlett.

'You're lying!' said Gerald. Then went on in a kind way, 'There are lots of other young men, Scarlett. I want you to be happy, and you wouldn't be happy with him.'

'Oh, I would! I would!'

'The Wilkes are different from other people,' said Gerald. 'They marry their cousins and keep their strangeness in the family. Look how they read books, and go to Boston and New York to see paintings and hear music.'

'Nobody rides a horse better than Ashley!' said Scarlett.

'Oh, yes, Ashley can ride and drink with the best of men, but he cares nothing about those things,' said Gerald. 'Now listen, there are other fine boys to marry, Scarlett. And when I'm gone, I'll leave Tara to you and –'

'I don't want Tara!' cried Scarlett, angrily. 'Plantations don't mean anything when –' She was going to say *when you don't have the man you want*, but Gerald's shout stopped her.

'Not mean anything! Land is the only thing in the world that *does* mean anything!' he cried. 'It will come to you, Scarlett, this love of the land. It's in your blood and there's no denying it.' He held her arm as they walked towards the house. 'I'll not worry your mother with this, and nor must you.'

They met Ellen O'Hara at the door. She was carrying the black bag in which she always kept the medicines she used for the slaves. Mammy was with her, and did not look pleased.

'Mr O'Hara,' Ellen said, 'a baby is dying at the Slattery house and Mammy and I are going to see what we can do.'

'The Slatterys!' shouted Gerald. 'Those white trash?'

'She is always nursin' negroes and white trash who could look after themselves,' said Mammy, annoyed.

'Take my place at supper, Scarlett,' said Ellen, touching her daughter's cheek. She was a tall woman, with a quiet, gentle voice and a warm smile that charmed everyone.

There was something magical about her mother's touch, thought Scarlett, and for a moment forgot all about Ashley.

But later an idea came to her. 'Ashley doesn't *know* I love him!' she thought. 'He thinks I love Brent or Stuart, and he's marrying Melanie because he thinks he can't have me! I must tell him, then we can run off to Jonesboro and get married! By this time tomorrow night, I might be Mrs Ashley Wilkes!'

Chapter 2 Rhett Butler

Early the next morning, Gerald told his plantation manager, Jonas Wilkerson, to pack his things and leave. Jonas, Ellen had discovered, was the father of Emmie Slattery's dead baby, and now Ellen would not have him working at Tara. Jonas was a Yankee and hated all Southerners, and he was angry at losing the best manager's job in the neighbourhood.

Ellen told Gerald that she was not going to the party at Twelve Oaks. 'I must check Jonas's figures in the plantation books,' she said. 'Mammy win stay and help me.'

So Gerald rode on his horse beside the carriage that took Scarlett and her two sisters down the road to Twelve Oaks.

Scarlett thought about her plans to marry Ashley. 'No one must suspect anything,' she thought, 'so I'll flirt with every man there, from old Frank Kennedy to shy Charlie Hamilton. It will be cruel to Ashley, but it will make him want me more.'

'I don't know why you look so happy this morning,' said her sister, Suellen, looking at Scarlett. 'You know Ashley's going to marry Melanie, Pa said so. And *I* know you love Ashley!'

'Suellen, that's not true!' said Careen, the youngest of the three. 'It's Brent that Scarlett cares about.'

The whole family knew that Careen loved Brent Tarleton. But he never gave her a thought except as Scarlett's baby sister. 'I don't care about Brent,' said Scarlett, smiling, 'and he doesn't care about me. He's waiting for you to grow up!'

Careen went red in the face, 'Oh, Scarlett, is he really?' she said.

They went over the hill, and saw Twelve Oaks. The house was white and beautiful under the blue sky. Lunch was going to be served outside, and Scarlett saw the Tarleton twins with their two brothers, Boyd and Tom; and Alex and Tony Fontaine; and the two Calvert boys, Raiford and Cade.

'Good! Everyone is here!' thought Scarlett.

John Wilkes stood on the entrance steps, a silver-haired man with a quiet charm that was as warm as a summer sun. Next to him was his daughter, Honey Wilkes. His other daughter, India, was nowhere to be seen, and Scarlett guessed that she was in the kitchen giving final orders to the servants.

'Poor India,' thought Scarlett. 'She's been so busy looking after Twelve Oaks since her mother died that she's had no time to catch any man except Stuart Tarleton, and it's not my problem if he thinks I'm prettier than her.'

John Wilkes helped Scarlett from the carriage, and Frank Kennedy hurried to give a helping hand to Suellen, who went red but looked delighted. Frank was forty, with a thin red beard. He was nervous with women and was surprised when Scarlett, remembering her plan, gave him one of her best smiles.

Stuart and Brent Tarleton moved towards her, and Scarlett looked around as she talked and laughed with them. Suddenly, she noticed a stranger standing alone. He looked at least thirty-five and was tall and strong, with a black moustache. Scarlett went red as he stared at her with a cool smile. Then he turned away as someone called, 'Rhett! Rhett Butler!'

Rhett Butler? Did she know the name? Scarlett's thoughts turned to Ashley and she forgot about the smiling man.

'I must go and comb my hair,' she told Stuart and Brent. 'You boys wait for me, and don't run off with any other girl!'

As she went up the wide stairs, a shy voice behind her called her name. Scarlett turned and saw Charles Hamilton, a nice-looking boy with soft brown hair and deep brown eyes.

She gave him her biggest smile. 'Why, Charles Hamilton, you handsome old thing! I'm sure you came all the way from Atlanta just to break my poor heart!'

Charles almost fainted. This was the way girls talked to other boys, not to him!

'Now you wait here until I come back,' said Scarlett. 'And don't talk to those other girls or I'll be very jealous!'

'I – I won't,' he said.

Scarlett saw Rhett Butler, a few feet away. He was smiling again, and had a strange look in his eye as he stared at her.

Scarlett went red again and hurried on up the stairs.

Cathleen Calvert was in the bedroom.

'Cathleen,' said Scarlett, 'who is that nasty man Butler?'

'My dear, don't you know?' whispered Cathleen, excitedly. 'He's from Charleston, but his family won't speak to him!'

'Really?' said Scarlett. 'Why?'

'He took a girl out riding in a carriage one afternoon and they stayed out nearly all night! When they finally arrived home, he said that the horse ran away and that they got lost in the forest. And guess what?'

'Tell me,' said Scarlett, hoping for the worst.

'He refused to marry her the next day!'

'Oh,' said Scarlett, disappointed.

'He said that he did nothing to her, but her brother invited him to fight – and Mr Butler shot him! Well, after that, Mr Butler had to leave Charleston.'

'Did she have a baby?' whispered Scarlett.

'No,' said Cathleen, 'but no one will ever marry her now.'

'I wish Ashley would stay out all night with me,' thought Scarlett. 'He's too much of a gentleman not to marry me afterwards.'

Chapter 3   Changes

Scarlett sat under a large tree, with her lunch on a plate in front of her. But although there were seven handsome young men sitting around her, Ashley was not one of them and she was not happy. He was sitting on the grass with Melanie Hamilton, talking quietly and smiling the slow, lazy smile that Scarlett loved. Melanie had dark hair and a heart-shaped face. She was small, but seemed older than her seventeen years.

Scarlett saw Rhett Butler talking to John Wilkes. He looked at her and laughed, and she had the feeling that this nasty man knew her true feelings about Ashley, and was amused.

It was two o'clock and the sun was warm. Scarlett was just wondering if India would suggest that the ladies went into the house, when she heard Gerald arguing with John Wilkes.

'Hope for peace with the Yankees?' Gerald was shouting. 'No, the South must show that it's strong and ready for a fight!'

Other men joined in the discussion. 'Of course we'll fight!' 'Yankee thieves!' 'One Southerner can fight twenty Yankees!'

Charles Hamilton found himself alone with Scarlett as the others moved away. 'Miss O'Hara,' he said, 'if I go to fight, will you be sorry?'

Scarlett thought men were stupid to think women were interested in these things, but she answered, 'I'll cry into my pillow every night,' not meaning a word of it.

'Miss O'Hara, I must tell you something,' said Charles, suddenly feeling brave. 'I – I love you! I want to marry you!'

Scarlett wanted to tell Charles he looked silly, but said automatically, 'This is so sudden. I don't know what to say.'

'I'll wait for ever!' cried Charles.

Scarlett noticed that Ashley was now with the group of men.

'If Georgia fights, I'll go with her,' Ashley was saying. 'But most of the sadness in the world was caused by wars, and when they were over, no one knew what they were about.'

More arguing burst out after this until Rhett Butler spoke. 'Gentlemen,' he said, 'can I say a word? There's not one gun factory in the South, and not a wool or cotton factory either. We haven't a single war-ship, and the Yankees could quickly stop us selling our cotton abroad with a blockade. They have all the things we haven't got, gentlemen. All we have is cotton and slaves – and brave talk!'

Everyone was shocked, but Scarlett could not help feeling he was right. She had never seen a factory, and did not know anyone who had. 'But he's no gentleman to say these things at a party, where everyone is having a good time,' she thought.

♦

It was late afternoon, and the ladies were resting in the six great bedrooms at Twelve Oaks, to be ready for the dance that evening. They had their dresses off, and most were asleep.

Scarlett checked that Melanie was lying down next to Honey Wilkes before she quietly left the room and went down the stairs. From a window, she saw Ashley drinking and talking with a group of men on the step outside. She walked silently across to the library. 'I'll wait in here until he comes into the house,' she thought, 'and then I'll call to him.'

The library was half-dark with the curtains closed to keep out the sun. Across the room was a sofa with its high back towards her, and around the walls were hundreds of books. Scarlett left the door open and tried to remember what she was going to say to Ashley. 'Perhaps it will help if I pray,' she thought, and closed her eyes.

'Scarlett!' It was Ashley's voice. She opened her eyes and saw him looking at her from the doorway. 'Are you hiding from Charles or the Tarletons?' he said.

She pulled him into the room.

'What is it?' he said. 'Have you got a secret to tell me?'

'Yes – a secret,' she said. 'I love you!'

He was silent, and there was a worried and confused look in his eyes. Then he made himself smile and said lightly, 'You have every other man's heart here today, Scarlett, isn't that enough? Do you want mine, too? Well, you've always had it.'

'He doesn't believe me!' she thought. 'He thinks I'm just flirting with him!' Scarlett looked into his eyes. 'Ashley! Tell me you love me, my dear!' she cried.

He put his hand across her lips. 'Don't say these things.'

'But I love you,' she cried, 'and I know you love me. Ashley, you do care, don't you?'

'Yes,' he said quietly. 'I care.'

'And you do want to marry me?' she said.

'I'm going to marry Melanie,' he replied. He took her hands in his. 'How can I make you understand, Scarlett? Love just isn't enough when two people are as different as we are.'

'But you said you cared for me,' said Scarlett.

'I was wrong to say it.'

She began to get angry. 'You're afraid to marry me!' she said, her voice getting louder. 'You'll marry that stupid little fool who can only say "No" and "Yes"!'

Ashley's face went white. 'Stop!' he said.

She pulled away from him. 'I'll hate you until I die!' she shouted, and she hit him hard across the face.

He said nothing, but lifted her hand to his lips and kissed it. Then he was gone, and the memory of the sad and hopeless look on his face would stay with her until the day she died.

Scarlett began to shake. 'Now he'll hate me,' she thought. 'Every time he looks at me he'll remember me saying all those things.' She began to feel hot all over. Did other people know how she felt about Ashley? Was everyone *laughing* at her?

Her hand dropped to a little table next to her, and her fingers closed around a pretty glass bowl. She picked it up and threw it wildly across the room. It missed the top of the sofa but crashed against the wall beyond.

'But I love you,' she cried, 'and I know you love me. Ashley,
you do care, don't you?'

'This,' said a voice from the other side of the sofa, 'is too much!' A man had been lying on it, but now he stood up.

It was Rhett Butler.

Scarlett almost fainted. 'Sir,' she said, 'you are no gentleman to listen to other people's conversations!'

'And you, Miss, are no lady,' he said. 'But ladies rarely interest me, and I cannot understand, my dear Miss O'Hara, what a wild and hot-blooded girl like you can find to like about the handsome but very boring Mr Wilkes.'

'You aren't good enough to clean his boots!' she shouted.

He laughed. 'And you were going to hate him all your life!'

She wanted to kill him, but she walked out of the room and pulled the heavy door shut behind her with a crash.

♦

A horse came fast towards the house, its rider low over the animal's back. Excitement was in every line of the man's face as he jumped down. The other men crowded round him, and he spoke quickly. Suddenly, Stuart Tarleton gave a shout.

Scarlett saw these things through a window as she went quietly back up the stairs. 'Somebody's house must be on fire,' she thought. She went on to the bedroom and was about to open the door when she heard voices inside.

'Scarlett flirted with every man here today,' Honey Wilkes was saying. 'She was certainly going after Charles, and you know Charles and I are going to be married.'

'Are you really!' whispered other voices excitedly.

'Yes, but don't tell anybody yet,' said Honey. 'But there's only one person Scarlett cares about — and that's Ashley!'

'Honey, you know that isn't true,' said Melanie. 'And it's so unkind to say it.'

'It is true! Scarlett took Stuart from India, and today she tried to take Mr Kennedy from Suellen. And Ashley —'

Scarlett ran back down the stairs. 'I must get home!' she thought. But when she was on the steps outside, she stopped. She couldn't go home! She couldn't run away and show them how ashamed she was feeling! It would only make things worse.

She hated them. She hated Ashley. She hated *everyone*!

'I'll stay and make them sorry,' she thought. 'I will!'

She turned towards the house – and saw Charles Hamilton.

'Do you know what's happened?' he cried.

She said nothing, only stared at him.

'Mr Lincoln called for soldiers!' he said. 'Seventy-five thousand of them! Of course, it will mean fighting, Miss Scarlett, but don't you worry, it'll be all over in a month.'

Scarlett was only half-listening. 'He has plenty of money,' she was thinking. 'He lives in Atlanta, and if I marry him quickly it will show Ashley that I don't care – that I was only flirting with him. And it will just *kill* Honey. She'll never get another man, and everyone will laugh at her! And it will hurt Melanie because she loves Charles so much.'

'Will you wait for me, Miss Scarlett?' Charles was saying.

Scarlett made a decision. 'I don't want to wait,' she said.

He held her hand, his mouth wide open. Twice he tried to say something, but the words wouldn't come. At last he said, 'Can – can you possibly love me?'

She said nothing but looked down at the floor, pretending to be shy. Charles wanted to shout and sing and kiss her, and then to tell everyone that Scarlett O'Hara loved him!

'Will you marry me soon?' he said, not daring to breathe.

'The sooner the better,' she said.

♦

Within two weeks, Ashley was married to Melanie, and Scarlett was married to Charles. Two months later she was a widow.

Charles died from typhoid. He never fought a battle. He never

15

got close to a Yankee. Soon after, Scarlett discovered that she was going to have a baby, and she became the mother of Charles' son. She called him Wade. She did not love or want the child, and it did not seem possible that he was hers.

Every time she thought of Ashley, she cried, and went back to her bed and refused to eat. Ellen tried to help but failed. And then Charles' aunt, Miss Pittypat Hamilton, wrote asking if Scarlett could come to Atlanta for a long visit. She and Melanie wanted very much to see Charlie's dear little baby.

So Scarlett went to Atlanta with Wade, and Prissy, her young slave. She did not want to go, but any change was welcome.

Chapter 4   Atlanta

The war was making Atlanta a busy city. Trains thundered in and out, and the narrow, muddy streets were full of army wagons and ambulances. Scarlett rode from the railway station in Miss Pittypat's carriage, with 'Uncle Peter', a tall, thin negro who was Aunt Pitty's old slave.

She saw a tall, handsome woman in a bright coloured dress, and with hair so red that it couldn't possibly be the real colour. 'Who is that, Uncle Peter?' she whispered.

'I don't know,' said Uncle Peter, looking away quickly.

'Yes, you do. Who is she?'

'Belle Watling,' he said after a moment. 'Miss Pitty ain't goin' to like you askin' questions about women like that.'

Scarlett was suddenly shocked. 'She must be a bad woman!' she thought, staring. She had never seen a prostitute before.

Miss Pittypat's red-brick house was on Peachtree Road, and Aunt Pitty was waiting excitedly on the front step. Melanie was with her and Scarlett saw the loving smile of welcome on the little heart-shaped face – and felt a rush of dislike.

This jealous dislike grew as the days went by, and sometimes Scarlett had to leave the room when Melanie talked about Ashley. But Atlanta was more interesting than Tara, and she was busy nursing at the hospital with Mrs Meade, the doctor's wife, and other women. All married women in Atlanta nursed the soldiers, and most were glad to do it. But Scarlett was a nurse only because she had to be.

'Melanie is content to stay at home and never go to parties, and to wear black for her brother when she's only eighteen years old,' thought Scarlett. 'But she was never popular like me and she doesn't miss the things I miss. And she's got Ashley and I haven't got anybody!' And she began to cry.

One afternoon, two ladies of the town – Mrs Merriwether and Mrs Elsing – visited Aunt Pitty.

'The McLure girls were called to Virginia to bring home their brother,' Mrs Elsing told them. 'He was hurt.'

'Pitty, we need you and Melanie to take their places at the sale tonight,' said Mrs Merriwether.

'Oh, but we can't go,' said Aunt Pitty. 'With poor Charlie dead only a –'

'Don't say "can't" to me, Pittypat Hamilton,' said Mrs Merriwether. 'We need you to watch the negroes with the food, and we need Melanie for the McLure girls' table. Just remember, it's to make money for the Cause!'★

'I think we should go,' said Scarlett suddenly, trying not to look too enthusiastic. 'We must do it for the hospital.'

They all looked surprised that it was Scarlett who offered, but Mrs Merriwether said, 'Scarlett's right. You must all come.'

♦

★ Cause: the one word used to describe all the reasons for the South going to war with the North.

Scarlett sat behind a table with Melanie at the sale. They were in a large room, which was usually full of soldiers learning the business of war. But tonight there were flowers and coloured lights around the room, and music was playing. There would be dancing soon, but already Scarlett's feet were secretly moving in time with the music.

Across the room, a tall man, dressed in black, with a fine white shirt, was staring at her. He smiled and she smiled back – until she remembered who he was, and then her hand flew to her mouth! It was Rhett Butler, and now he was coming over!

'I did not think you would remember me, Miss O'Hara,' he said. There was laughter in his eyes, and Scarlett's face went bright red as she remembered their last meeting.

Melanie turned at the sound of his voice. 'Oh, it's Mr Rhett Butler, isn't it?' she said, smiling. 'I met you –'

'At Twelve Oaks,' he finished for her.

'What are you doing so far from Charleston, Mr Butler?'

'Business,' he said. 'I find I must not only bring things into your city but must also stay here to sell them.

Melanie gave him a delighted smile. 'You must be the famous Captain Butler we've heard so much about – the blockade runner. Scarlett, what's the matter? Are you feeling faint?'

Scarlett sat down on a chair. 'Of all the people to come here,' she was thinking, 'why did *he* have to come?'

'It's quite warm in here,' Rhett was saying. 'Can I take you across to a window, Miss O'Hara?'

'No,' said Scarlett, so rudely that Melanie stared.

'She's not Miss O'Hara any longer,' said Melanie, smiling in a kind way. 'She is Mrs Hamilton, and my sister now.'

'Oh,' said Rhett, looking closely at Scarlett. 'And are your husbands here tonight?'

'My husband is in Virginia,' said Melanie, proudly. 'But Charles –' She could not go on.

'Charles is dead,' said Scarlett.

'My dear ladies!' said Rhett. 'I'm so sorry. But to die for one's country is to live for ever.'

Melanie smiled at him through her tears while Scarlett felt herself hating him. 'He doesn't mean a word,' she thought.

Melanie forgot about Captain Butler and Scarlett as customers crowded round her table. Scarlett sat quietly on her chair, wishing that Captain Butler was back on his ship.

'Has your husband been dead long?' he asked her.

'Yes, almost a year.'

'And this is the first time –?'

'I know it looks strange,' she said. 'but the McLure girls couldn't come, so Melanie and I came –'

'For the Cause,' he finished for her.

'Why does he make it sound so cheap?' thought Scarlett. When Mrs Merriwether spoke of 'the Cause', she spoke proudly. Scarlett wanted to tell him this but then remembered she was only here because she was tired of sitting at home.

He seemed to guess her thoughts, because he said, 'Would you be here if the Confederacy didn't need you, Mrs Hamilton?'

'Of course not,' said Scarlett. 'People would think I hadn't loved –' And she stopped. She could not pretend to him that she had loved Charlie, not after the things he had heard in the library at Twelve Oaks.

He moved close to her. 'Don't worry.' he whispered. 'Your guilty secret is safe with me!'

'How can you say those things!' she said, angrily. But then she looked at him, saw the laughter in his eyes and realized he was joking with her – and she found herself laughing, too.

Several people near them were shocked to see Charles' widow laughing with a strange man, and began to whisper about it.

Dr Meade called for everyone to be quiet. 'Gentlemen,' he

said, 'if you want to dance with a lady this evening, you must pay for her! Remember, all the money is for the Cause!'

The young girls whispered excitedly, while the men laughed.

'Oh, if only I could wear an apple-green dress and have flowers in my hair!' thought Scarlett. 'Twenty men would fight to dance with me and pay their money to the doctor!'

Rhett Butler was watching her. Suddenly, he called out: 'Mrs Charles Hamilton – one hundred and fifty dollars in gold!'

Scarlett was so surprised, she could not move. Everyone looked at her, and she saw the doctor whisper to Rhett Butler, probably telling him that widows could not dance.

'Another one of our young ladies, perhaps?' said Dr Meade.

'No,' said Rhett. 'Mrs Hamilton.'

'Impossible,' said the doctor. 'Mrs Hamilton will not –'

'Yes, I will!' Scarlett heard herself shout.

She saw the shocked faces of Melanie and the older women; she saw the surprised and annoyed faces of the younger girls. But Scarlett didn't care. She was going to dance again!

'I – I'm doing it for the Cause,' Scarlett told Rhett, and he began to laugh. 'Stop laughing, everyone is looking at us!'

'Do you care if people talk?' said Rhett.

'No – but – well, a nice girl is supposed to care.' She changed the subject. 'Tell me, do you have a lot of money?'

'What a rude question, Mrs Hamilton!' he laughed. 'But the answer is yes, and I'll make a million on the blockade. One can always make money from a war, whether one is on the winning side or not.'

'Do you think the Confederacy will lose?'

'Yes,' he said.

'Oh, well, these things bore me,' said Scarlett. 'Captain Butler, don't hold me so tightly, people are looking.'

'If no one was looking, would you care?' he said, smiling.

'Captain Butler!' she said, pretending to be shocked. Then

*She saw the shocked faces of Melanie and the older women;
she saw the surprised faces of the younger girls.*

added, 'You dance very well for a big man, but it will be years and years before I'll dance again.'

'I'll offer more money for you in the next dance,' he said, 'and the next, and the next.'

'Oh, it's the end of the music,' said Scarlett. 'And here's Aunt Pittypat coming out of the back room. I suppose Mrs Merriwether told her. Her eyes are as big as saucers.'

♦

'I don't care if they talk,' said Scarlett, next morning. 'I'm sure I made more money for the hospital than any girl there.'

'What does the money matter?' cried Aunt Pitty. 'Poor Charlie dead only a year! And that Captain Butler is a terrible person, Scarlett.'

'I can't believe he's all that bad,' said Melanie, gently. 'When you think how brave he's been, running the blockade –'

'He isn't brave,' said Scarlett. 'He does it for money. He doesn't care about the Confederacy, and he says we're going to lose. But he dances wonderfully.'

Pittypat and Melanie were so shocked they could not speak.

'I'm tired of sitting at home and I'm not going to do it any more,' Scarlett went on. 'If they all talked about me last night, then it won't matter what they say about me now.'

Melanie put her arm round Scarlett. 'You did a brave thing last night,' she said, 'and it's going to help the hospital a lot. Aunt Pitty, it's been difficult for Scarlett. And war times aren't like other times. Think of all the soldiers who are far from home and without friends. We've been selfish. We must have a soldier here to dinner every Sunday from now on.'

22

Chapter 5   Heroes

The autumn of 1862 went quickly for Scarlett, with nursing, parties and visits to Tara. The visits to Tara were disappointing, because Ellen worked from morning until night, and Gerald was busy because he could not get a manager to take Jonas Wilkerson's place. Suellen was waiting for the war to end so that she could marry Frank Kennedy, and Careen dreamed about Brent Tarleton. So Scarlett was never sorry to return from Tara to Atlanta.

There were many things she did not tell Ellen, but her biggest secret was that Rhett Butler called at Aunt Pittypat's house whenever he was in town. Scarlett went riding with him in his carriage, and he took her to dances and sales. She looked forward to his visits because there was something exciting about him, something different from any other man she knew. 'It's as if I'm in love with him!' she thought. 'But I'm not.'

He sat and listened to Melanie for hours as she talked about Ashley and how proud she was of him. 'But *I* only have to say Ashley's name and he smiles nastily at me!' thought Scarlett.

'Why are you nicer to Melanie than to me?' she asked him one day. 'I'm much prettier than she is.'

'Dare I hope that you're jealous?' he said, smiling.

'Don't be silly!' she said.

'Another hope gone! If I am "nicer" to Mrs Wilkes, it's because she is one of the very few kind and unselfish people I know. And, although she is still young, she is one of the few great ladies I have been lucky enough to meet.'

'Don't you think I'm a great lady, too?' said Scarlett.

'My dear, I think we agreed when we first met that you were no lady at all,' said Rhett.

'Oh, you rude, horrible man, reminding me of that again!' she said. But he only laughed at her.

The older men and women in Atlanta did not like Rhett, but they agreed that he was brave. But when they told him this, he replied that he was as frightened as the 'brave boys' who were fighting. This annoyed them because everyone knew there wasn't a cowardly Confederate soldier anywhere. He always said 'our brave boys' or 'our heroes in grey', but made it sound like an insult. And when young ladies thanked him for being one of the heroes who fought for them, he smiled and said that he would do the same thing for Yankee women if the Yankees paid him enough money.

At an evening of music at Mrs Elsing's home, Rhett was talking with a group of men when Scarlett heard an angry voice arguing with him, 'Are you saying, sir, that the Cause for which our heroes are dying is not sacred?'

'All wars are sacred to those who have to fight them,' replied Rhett, in a bored and lazy voice. 'If the people who started wars didn't pretend they were sacred, who would be foolish enough to fight? No, it's money that wars are really fought about, but few people realize it. Their ears are too full of fine words from stay-at-home speakers.'

And before Scarlett could reach him, he was leaving.

'Let him go,' said Mrs Elsing, holding her arm. 'He's not one of us. He's a snake-in-the-grass who we were foolish enough to invite into our homes!'

Later, Mrs Merriwether rode home in Aunt Pitty's carriage, and immediately said what she thought. 'He insulted us all and the Confederacy, too,' she said. 'Saying that we were fighting for money! Saying that our leaders have lied to us! Pitty, you must never let that man into your house again!' She turned to Scarlett and Melanie. 'And I don't want to hear you two girls speaking to him again – Melanie, what's the matter?'

24

Melanie was white and her eyes were wide open. 'I *will* speak to him again,' she said in a low voice. 'I will not be rude to him. I will not tell him to stay away from the house.'

Mrs Merriwether's mouth fell open, and Aunt Pitty's did the same. Uncle Peter turned to stare.

'Now why didn't *I* say that?' thought Scarlett.

Melanie's hands were shaking but she went on quickly. 'I won't be rude to him because of what he said, because it's – it's what Ashley thinks.'

'Melanie Hamilton, that's a lie!' said Mrs Merriwether. 'There was never a Wilkes who was a coward –'

'I never said Ashley was a coward,' said Melanie. 'I said he thinks what Captain Butler thinks, and he does. But he says it differently. In his letters, Ashley says we should not be fighting the Yankees. He says war isn't wonderful or sacred or any of those things, it's just dirty and useless and a terrible waste of men's lives.'

Scarlett said nothing. She was shocked to realize anyone as perfect as Ashley could think the same as a man like Rhett Butler. 'They both understand what is true about the war,' she thought, 'but Ashley will fight and die for it and Rhett won't. I think that shows Rhett is sensible.'

It was all very confusing.

Chapter 6   Missing

In the early part of 1863, the war went well for the Confederacy, but on the fourth day of July, there was news about hard fighting in Pennsylvania, near a little town called Gettysburg. The news came slowly, and fear began to spread across the town. Mothers prayed that their boys were not in Pennsylvania, but those who knew their relations were fighting next to Dr Meade's son,

Darcy, said they were proud for them to be in the big fight that would win the war.

In Aunt Pitty's house, the three women looked into each other's eyes with fear. Ashley was fighting with Darcy.

People waited outside the newspaper office for news. Scarlett, Melanie and Aunt Pitty came and waited in their carriage. Scarlett saw Mrs Meade with her youngest son, Phil, waiting for news of Darcy. Then the crowd began to move as Rhett Butler came through on his horse.

'The first lists will be out soon,' he said. 'Yes, look!'

The side window of the newspaper office opened and a hand came out. In it were the lists of the dead – long, narrow pieces of paper with the names close together. The crowd began to fight for them and there were shouts of, 'Let me through!'

Rhett got off his horse and pushed his way forward, his heavy shoulders above the rest of the crowd. Then he was back with five or six lists in his hand. He gave one to Melanie, and the others to the ladies in the carriages near him.

Melanie's hands shook so much that she gave the list to Scarlett, who quickly began to read. 'White ... Wilkins ... Winn ... Zebulon ... Oh, Melanie, he's not on it! He's not on it!'

Melanie began to cry with happiness, while Scarlett's heart seemed ready to burst. Ashley was alive! Ashley was alive!

Mrs Meade sat in her carriage and looked across at Melanie. 'Darcy won't need those new boots now,' she said.

'Oh, my dear!' cried Melanie, and jumped from her carriage.

'Mother, you've still got me,' said Phil. 'And if you'll just let me, I'll go and kill all the Yankees –'

'No!' cried Mrs Meade.

'Phil Meade, don't talk like that!' said Melanie, climbing in with Mrs Meade. 'Drive us home. Captain Butler, can you tell the doctor? He's at the hospital.'

Scarlett looked at the list again. So many names from Atlanta, and from all of Georgia. Calvert – Fontaine – Munroe. And surely there couldn't be *three* Tarletons! But there were. 'Tarleton – Brenton, Stuart and Thomas.' And Boyd killed the first year somewhere in Virginia. All the Tarleton boys gone!

'I'm sorry, Scarlett,' said Rhett. 'Many of your friends?'

'Yes,' she said. 'Oh, Rhett, why do there have to be wars? Why didn't the Yankees just pay for the negroes? Or why didn't we just give them the negroes for nothing?'

'It isn't about the negroes, Scarlett,' he said. 'They were just the excuse. There'll always be wars because men love wars.' He turned away. 'Now, I'm going to find Dr Meade.'

♦

After losing the battle of Gettysburg, the tired and much smaller Confederate army were pushed back into Virginia for the winter. As Christmas got closer, Ashley came home for a week. His father and his sisters – Honey and India – came to Atlanta to join him and Melanie.

Scarlett wanted to cry with happiness when she saw him. There was something new and strange in the lines of his sun-burned face. He was the same handsome Ashley, but much more exciting! He looked at her and said, 'Oh, Scarlett! You pretty, pretty thing!' and kissed her on the cheek.

Each day she tried to speak to Ashley alone, but Melanie was always with him. They all had questions to ask him about the war but, although he told them jokes and funny stories about friends, it seemed to Scarlett that he did this to stop them asking the questions he did not want to answer.

The week passed quickly, and Ashley had to return to Virginia. He said goodbye to Melanie in their room, and then Scarlett was at last able to see him alone.

'Ashley, may I go to the station with you?' she asked him.

'Father and the girls will be there,' he said. 'I want to remember you saying goodbye here. Will you let me do that?'

'Ashley, I'd do anything for you,' she said.

'Would you?' he said. 'There's something you can do for me.'

'What is it?' she asked, happily.

'Will you look after Melanie for me?' he said.

'Look after Melanie?' she said, disappointed.

'She loves you so much,' he said. 'Scarlett, when I think of what might happen to her if I was killed –'

'Don't say it!' she said. 'It's bad luck to speak of death!'

'I can't tell what will happen to me or to any of us,' said Ashley. 'But when the end comes, if I'm alive, I'll be far away from here. Too far to look after Melanie.'

'The – the end?' said Scarlett.

'The end of the war – and the end of the world.'

'Ashley, surely you don't think the Yankees will win.'

'All this week I've talked lies,' he said, 'I didn't want to frighten Melanie or Aunt Pitty. But yes, Scarlett, I think the Yankees will win. Gettysburg was the beginning of the end.'

'I couldn't live if you were dead!' she thought wildly.

'Don't repeat what I've said,' he told her. 'I don't want to frighten the others. You're strong, and it will be good to know that you and Melanie are together if anything happens to me. You will promise, won't you?'

'Oh, yes!' she cried, ready to promise him anything. 'Ashley! I can't let you go away! I can't be brave about it!'

'You must be brave,' he said. He took her face in his hands and kissed her lightly. 'Scarlett! Scarlett! You're so fine and good and strong. So beautiful – not just your sweet face, my dear, but your mind and your body.'

'Oh, Ashley,' she whispered happily, waiting for him to say

28

the three magic words 'I love you'. But they didn't come. Instead, she heard Uncle Peter with the carriage outside.

'Goodbye,' Ashley said softly.

'Kiss me,' she whispered. 'Kiss me goodbye.'

At the first touch of his lips on hers, she threw her arms around his neck and pulled him to her. For a moment he held her close, but then quickly pushed her away.

'No, Scarlett, no,' he said in a low voice.

'I love you!' she cried. 'Ashley, say you love me!'

She looked into his face – and it was the unhappiest face she was ever to see. 'Goodbye!' he said, his voice a whisper.

◆

For the next two months, Scarlett was happy. She had felt the quickness of Ashley's heart when her arms went round his neck. She had seen the look on his face. Oh, he loved her! She was sure of this now, and could almost feel sorry for Melanie.

But then in March Melanie said that she was going to have a baby, and a sharp pain cut right through Scarlett.

'Dr Meade says it will be here in late August or September,' Melanie said happily. 'Oh, Scarlett, isn't it wonderful?'

'Dear God!' thought Scarlett. 'A baby! Ashley's baby. Oh, how *could* he when he loves me and not Melanie? I can't go on living here now. I'll go home to Tara.'

And the next morning she got up intending to pack her things, but something happened that stopped her.

News came that Ashley was missing. He'd been missing for three days, after going on a five-man search to discover where the Yankee army were preparing to fight their next battle.

A shocked Scarlett was certain that God was punishing her for loving a married man. Melanie's face was white and frightened, like a child lost in the dark.

'Scarlett,' she said. 'You're all I've got now. Oh, I know Ashley is dead!' Suddenly, she was in Scarlett's arms, and they were crying and holding each other close.

'At least I've got his baby,' whispered Melanie.

'And I've got nothing,' thought Scarlett. 'Nothing but the look on his face when he said goodbye.'

♦

The first reports were 'Missing – believed killed,' but they changed to 'Missing – believed to be a prisoner.' Melanie, her hopes alive again, met every train, praying for a letter. She refused to obey Dr Meade and stay in bed, and one afternoon she fainted at the station and Rhett Butler brought her home.

'Mrs Wilkes, you're going to have a baby, aren't you?' he said. And when she gave an embarrassed nod, he went on, 'Then you must take better care of yourself or you'll harm the baby. I'll talk to some people I know in Washington. If Mr Wilkes is a prisoner, he'll be on a prisoners' list, and if he isn't – well, there's nothing worse than not knowing. But you must promise me you'll take care of yourself, or I won't help.'

'Oh, you're so kind,' cried Melanie.

A month later, Rhett brought news that Ashley was not dead but at Rock Island, a cruel and terrible prison in Illinois where many men would die before the end of the war.

'He had a chance to get out, but refused it,' said Rhett. 'The Yankees need men to fight the Indians in the West, and any prisoner who will join the Yankee army and fight the Indians for two years can get out of prison.'

'Why didn't he do that?' cried Scarlett. 'Why didn't he join, and then run away and come home as soon as he got out?'

Melanie became angry. 'How can you suggest that? I'd prefer to know he was dead at Rock Island than he was no longer a Confederate but a *Yankee* soldier! Of course he refused.'

When Scarlett was alone with Rhett, she asked, 'Wouldn't

you join the Yankees to get out of that place, and then run away?'

'Of course,' said Rhett, with a cold smile.

'Then why didn't Ashley?' said Scarlett.

'He's a gentleman,' said Rhett – meaning Ashley was a fool.

Chapter 7 News from Tara

That summer, for the first time since the war began, the people of Atlanta heard the sound of battle. The Yankees were getting closer! Many old men, like John Wilkes, and young boys, like Phil Meade, were sent to guard the bridges at Chattahoochee River, at the back of the main Confederate army.

Then, on a hot July afternoon, after a terrible battle at Peachtree Creek, a stream of Confederate soldiers began to arrive in Atlanta. Some were covered in blood, others helped those who couldn't walk to get to the hospitals.

Within days, the Yankees were on three sides of Atlanta, and the railway to Tennessee was under Yankee control. Only one railway to the south, to Macon, was still open. But if they could hold it, Atlanta could stand against the Yankees.

But when shells began to fall in the streets, women, children and old people began leaving the city. Mrs Elsing and Mrs Merriwether refused to leave. They were needed at the hospital, they said proudly, and no Yankee was going to run them out of their homes. Mrs Meade also refused. Phil was fighting not far away and she wanted to be near. Aunt Pitty was among the first to leave. She went to Macon to stay with a cousin. 'You girls should come with me,' she said.

But Scarlett did not like Aunt Pitty's cousin. 'I'll go to Tara, and Melanie can go to Macon with you,' she said.

'Scarlett, don't leave me!' cried Melanie. 'I'll die if you aren't with me when the baby comes! You promised Ashley that you'd take care of me. He told me he was going to ask you.'

'I'll keep my promise,' Scarlett said, tiredly, 'but I won't go to Macon. I'll go home to Tara, and you can come with me.'

But Dr Meade stopped Melanie going to Macon or Tara. 'You cannot travel,' he said. 'It might be dangerous. Miss Pitty, you go to Macon and leave the young ladies here. Miss Melanie, you must stay in bed until the baby comes.'

He spoke privately to Scarlett 'She is going to have a difficult time,' he said. 'You must stay with her until the baby comes. With these shells falling, it may be at any time.'

So Aunt Pitty went to Macon, taking Uncle Peter with her. And Scarlett and Melanie were left alone in Atlanta with Wade and Prissy.

♦

Those first days, Scarlett would not go into the streets. Every time she heard the scream of a shell coming, she rushed to Melanie's room and threw herself on the bed, and the two of them hid their heads in the pillow. Prissy and Wade hid under a table downstairs, Wade crying and Prissy screaming.

'I'd rather let Melanie die than go out and find the doctor when the shells are falling,' thought Scarlett.

But Prissy calmed Scarlett's fears. 'Don' you worry, Miss Scarlett. I know all about deliverin' babies,' she said. 'Ain't my mother told me all about it? Jus' leave it to me.'

At the end of July, Scarlett received a letter from Gerald telling her that Careen was ill with typhoid and that Scarlett must not come home. That night, she sat outside the house and thought of Tara. Life there would never be the same. She would never again hear the wild, happy voices of the Tarleton boys. Or the Munroe boys, or little Joe Fontaine, or –

The front gate opened and she quickly brushed tears from her face before looking up.

It was Rhett Butler. 'So you didn't go to Macon,' he said. 'Why did you stay?'

'To be with Melanie. She — well, she can't go just now.'

'Is Mrs Wilkes still here?' he said. He lit a cigar. 'And you stayed with her. How strange.'

'I see nothing strange about it,' she said, uncomfortably.

'You think Mrs Wilkes is silly and stupid,' he said. 'So why do you stay when there are Yankee shells falling all around?'

'Because she's Charlie's sister and — and like a sister to me,' said Scarlett, her cheeks getting hot.

'You mean because she's Ashley Wilkes' widow,' said Rhett.

Scarlett became angry. She liked to think she was a mystery to men, but Rhett could see through her like glass.

He took her hand in his. 'How lucky, to find you alone,' he said, and something in his voice made her face go hot again.

'He's going to tell me he loves me!' she thought. 'Then I can tell him he's wasting his time, and he'll feel a fool!'

He kissed her hand, and something electric passed through her whole body as his warm mouth touched her skin. 'I'm not in love with him,' she told herself. 'I'm in love with Ashley.'

'Scarlett, you do like me, don't you?' he said.

'Well . . . sometimes,' she said.

'Could you ever love me?'

'I've got him!' she thought, and answered in a cool voice. 'Certainly not! Not until you behave like a real gentleman.'

'And I don't intend to do that,' he said. 'So you don't love me? Good, because although I like you, Scarlett, I don't love you, and I didn't want to be the *second* man not to return your love, my dear.'

'You — you don't love me?' she said.

'Did you hope that I did? I'm sorry. But I do like you a lot. I know you still think lovingly of the wooden-headed Mr Wilkes, who has probably been dead these last six months. But there must be room in your heart for me, too. Scarlett, I want you more than I've ever wanted any woman.'

Scarlett was surprised and confused. 'Are you asking me to marry you?' she said.

He dropped her hand and laughed loudly. 'No, I'm not a marrying man, didn't I tell you that?'

'But – but – what –?'

'My dear,' he said quietly. 'I'm asking you to be my lover.'

Lover! Scarlett felt shock and disappointment at the same time. 'Get out!' she cried. 'Get out and don't ever come back! I'll – I'll tell my father, and he'll kill you!'

She watched him smile. He was not ashamed, he was amused! She ran into the house and tried to crash the door shut behind her, but it was too heavy.

'May I help you?' he asked.

And he crashed it shut for her as she ran upstairs.

♦

As the hot, noisy days of August came to an end, the shelling stopped. Then worrying news came from the south. The Yankees were trying to take the railway at Jonesboro, and Tara was close to the fighting. Eventually a soldier came to say that the Confederate army had pushed the Yankees back, but the railway was damaged and it would be some time before trains could travel again. He brought Scarlett a letter from her father, after meeting him in Jonesboro, and was able to tell her that the Yankees hadn't got to Tara.

'But what was Pa doing in Jonesboro?' she asked.

The soldier looked nervous. 'He – he was looking for an army doctor to go to Tara with him,' he said.

Scarlett opened her father's letter and began to read:

Dear Daughter, Your mother and both girls have typhoid and are very ill, but we must hope for the best. When your mother went to her bed, she told me to write and say that you must not come home and put yourself and Wade in danger, too. She sends her love and asks you to pray for her.

For the next week, Scarlett waited nervously for more news, but none came. No one knew where the Confederates were, or what the Yankees were doing. She had seen enough typhoid in the Atlanta hospitals to know that a week was a long time with that terrible illness, and she wanted to be at home. 'Oh, why doesn't this baby come?' she thought.

The last day of August arrived, and with it came rumours of a big battle south of Atlanta. People waited for news. If the Yankees won the Macon railway, they would soon be in Atlanta!

On the first of September, Scarlett woke to hear a sound like distant thunder. 'Rain coming,' she thought at first. Then she went to the window. 'No, not rain, guns! And from the south!' There lay Jonesboro, Tara – and her mother.

Scarlett went to Melanie's room. Melanie was in bed, her eyes closed and with dark circles around them. She looked worse than any sick person Scarlett had ever seen. Then her eyes opened and a soft warm smile lit her face.

'Scarlett,' she said. 'There's something I want to ask you.' Scarlett sat down on the bed and Melanie held her hand.

'I'm sorry about the guns, dear,' said Melanie. 'They're towards Jonesboro, aren't they? I know how worried you are. You could be at home if it weren't for me, couldn't you?'

'Yes,' said Scarlett, rudely.

'You're so good to me, and I love you for it. If I die, I want you to take my baby. Will you do that?'

Scarlett pulled her hand away, frightened. 'Don't be silly, Melanie,' she said. 'You're not going to die.'

'Promise me, Scarlett, then I won't be afraid,' said Melanie. 'I'm sure my baby will come today.'

35

'Oh, all right, I promise,' said Scarlett. 'Why do you think it will come today?'

'I've been having pains.'

'I'll send Prissy for Dr Meade,' said Scarlett.

'No, you know how busy he is. Just send for Mrs Meade.'

Chapter 8   The Yankees Are Coming

Scarlett sent Prissy for Mrs Meade and, after a long time, the little black girl returned alone.

'She wasn't there,' said Prissy. 'She got news that Mr Phil was shot an' she went with a carriage to fetch him home.'

Scarlett stared, wanting to shake her. 'Well, don't just stand there, go and fetch Mrs Merriwether!'

'She ain't there,' said Prissy. 'I stopped on my way home, but the house was shut up. She's probably at the hospital.'

Scarlett thought for a moment. 'Go to Mrs Elsing and explain everything,' she said. 'Ask her to come. And hurry!'

She went back to Melanie's room where Melanie was lying on her side, her face white. 'Mrs Meade is at the hospital,' lied Scarlett. She didn't want to worry Melanie by telling her about Phil getting shot. 'But Mrs Elsing is coming.'

It was an hour before Prissy came back, walking slowly along the road. Scarlett hurried out to meet her.

'Mrs Elsing is over at the hospital,' said Prissy. 'A lot of soldiers came in on the early train, most of them hurt bad –'

'You must go to the hospital,' said Scarlett. 'I'll give you a letter for Dr Meade, but if he isn't there, give it to one of the other doctors. And hurry back this time!'

Minutes later, Prissy went off with a letter and Scarlett went back upstairs. Melanie asked no questions, but her face was fun of pain. An hour passed and then another. Afternoon came, and

Melanie's pains were worse. Where was Prissy? Why didn't she come? Scarlett went to the window. Had the sound of the guns died away, or was it her imagination? Then she saw Prissy running down the street, fear written all over her little black face. Scarlett quickly moved from the window.

'I'll get some cooler water,' she told Melanie.

She got downstairs as Prissy came in. 'They're fightin' at Jonesboro, Miss Scarlett! They say we're losin' the war!'

'Where's Dr Meade? When is he conning?' said Scarlett.

'He ain't at the hospital. Mrs Merriwether and Mrs Elsin' ain't there either. A man told me the doctor was down at the railway station with the soldiers from Jonesboro. But, Miss Scarlett, I was too frightened to go down there. People are dyin' down there, and I'm frightened of dead people.'

'What about the other doctors?' asked Scarlett.

'Miss Scarlett, I couldn't get them to read your letter,' said Prissy. 'They're workin' in the hospital like they're all crazy! "Don't worry me about babies when we've got men dyin' here!" one of them shouted at me.'

'Listen,' said Scarlett. 'I'll get Dr Meade and you sit with Miss Melanie. Don't tell her where the fighting is, and don't tell her that the other doctors won't come, do you hear?'

Scarlett hurried out of the house and into the hot sun. A soldier came riding past and she stopped him.

'Are the Yankees coming?' she asked him.

'Yes, Miss,' he said. 'The army are leaving Atlanta soon.'

Scarlett began to run. People rushed past her as she pushed her way through the crowd and on towards the station. But as she went round the side of the Atlanta Hotel, she stopped.

There, lying on the ground under the heat of the sun, were hundreds and hundreds of men. Some were screaming with pain. There was blood everywhere, and the smell of unwashed bodies came to meet her. She put a hand across her mouth and nose.

Then she lifted her skirts and stepped over dead men, and men with blood on their uniforms, and men making sounds which had to mean: 'Water! Water!'

'Dr Meade!' cried Scarlett. 'Is Dr Meade here?'

A man looked up. It was the doctor. His shirt and trousers were red with blood, and his face was grey with tiredness.

'Thank God you're here,' he said to Scarlett. 'I can use every pair of hands. Quickly, come here!'

She went to him as fast as she could across the rows of bodies. 'Doctor, you must come! Melanie is having her baby!'

'Baby?' thundered the doctor. 'Are you crazy? I can't leave these men. Get some woman to help you. Get my wife.'

She started to tell him why Mrs Meade could not come – then stopped. She could not tell him his son was hurt.

'Doctor, please!' she cried. 'Please come!'

He looked at her. 'The Yankees are coming and the army is moving out of town. I don't know what they'll do with these men. There aren't any trains. The Macon line is under Yankee control. Listen, I can't promise, Scarlett, but I'll try.'

Scarlett went back through the rows of men. On the streets beyond the Atlanta Hotel, soldiers were moving out of the city. There seemed to be thousands of them. Wagons went past, throwing up clouds of dust. There were drunken women with painted faces among the crowd. Scarlett saw Belle Watling, and heard her drunken laugh as she held on to a one-armed soldier.

Scarlett began to run again. When she got back to the house, Wade was waiting outside.

'Wade hungry,' he cried.

'Be quiet!' said Scarlett. 'Go and play in the back garden.' She looked up and saw Prissy at the bedroom window. Scarlett waved at her to come down, then went into the house. Prissy came down the stairs three at a time.

On the streets beyond the Atlanta Hotel,
soldiers were moving out of the city.

'The doctors can't come,' said Scarlett. 'You've got to deliver the baby, and I'll help you.'

Prissy's mouth fell open.

'What's the matter?' said Scarlett.

'I – Miss Scarlett – I don't know nothin' about deliverin' babies,' said Prissy, looking at the floor.

Scarlett took Prissy's arm and squeezed it. 'You black liar! What do you mean? You said you knew everything about –'

'I was lyin', Miss Scarlett!' cried Prissy.

Scarlett had never hit a slave in all her life, but she hit Prissy's black cheek as hard as she could. Prissy screamed loudly and tried to pull away.

'Scarlett, is it you?' Melanie's weak voice came from upstairs. 'Please come! Please!'

Scarlett tried to remember what Mammy and Ellen did when Wade was born. 'Build a fire and make sure there's plenty of water,' she told Prissy. 'Bring all the towels you can find, and some string and a pair of scissors. Quickly!'

She pushed Prissy towards the kitchen, then took a deep breath before going upstairs.

◆

There was never an afternoon as long as this one. Or as hot. Scarlett pulled the bedroom curtains across to keep out the sun. Melanie tried to be brave, but when evening came, she began calling for Ashley – over and over – until Scarlett wanted to cover her face with a pillow. 'Perhaps the doctor will come after all,' thought Scarlett, and she told Prissy to go to the Meades' house and see if he or Mrs Meade were there.

Prissy went, but came back soon after, alone.

'The doctor ain't been home all day,' she reported. 'An', Miss Scarlett, Mr Phil is dead. He was shot. I didn't see Mrs Meade because she was gettin' his body ready for –'

'All right,' said Scarlett quickly.

Melanie opened her eyes and whispered, 'Are the Yankees coming?'

'No,' said Scarlett. 'Prissy's a liar.'

'Yes, Miss, I am,' agreed Prissy.

'The Yankees are coming,' whispered Melanie, guessing correctly. 'My poor baby. Scarlett, you mustn't stay here.'

'You know I won't leave you,' said Scarlett.

'Why not?' said Melanie. 'I'm going to die anyway.'

Chapter 9   Escape from Atlanta

Scarlett came down the dark stairs slowly, like an old woman. She went outside and sat on the front step. It was all over. Melanie was not dead, and Prissy was giving the small baby boy his first bath while Melanie was asleep.

The night air was cool and fresh on her face and arms. More soldiers were leaving the city, passing by the house, although she could not see them clearly in the darkness.

What could she do? Where could she turn for help? Scarlett remembered Rhett. He was strong and clever, and he wasn't afraid of the Yankees. And he had a horse and carriage, too.

She called Prissy. 'Captain Butler lives at the Atlanta Hotel,' she said. 'Go there quickly and tell him about the baby. Tell him that I want him to get us out of here.'

'Suppose Cap'n Butler ain't at the hotel?' said Prissy.

'Go to the bar-rooms, go to Belle Watling's house,' said Scarlett. 'Just find him, or the Yankees will get us all!'

Scarlett went back into the house and waited. After some time, she saw that the sky was becoming pink over the east of the city. Then a large flame shot high into the darkness.

'The Yankees are burning the city!' she thought.

Moments later, Prissy ran into the room.

'The Yankees −?' Scarlett began.

'No, it's our men,' said Prissy. 'They're burnin' the gun factory, an' what the army left. We're all goin' to burn up!'

'Did you see Captain Butler?' said Scarlett.

'Yes, I saw him, an' I says "Come quick, Cap'n Butler, an' bring your horse an' carriage." An' he says they took his horse but he'll steal another one.'

'He's coming? He's going to bring a horse?'

'So he says.'

Scarlett began to feel better. She would forgive Rhett anything if he got them out of this mess. 'Wake up Wade and dress him,' she told Prissy. 'Then pack some clothes for all of us. Don't tell Miss Melanie we're going, not yet, but put two thick towels around the baby and pack his clothes, too.'

It seemed hours before Rhett finally came with a wagon. He was dressed as if he was going dancing, in a white coat and trousers. He carried two guns, and his pockets were full of bullets.

'Good evening,' he said, smiling and taking off his hat. 'Fine weather we're having! I hear you're going on a trip.'

'If you make any jokes, I'll never speak to you again,' said Scarlett, her voice shaking.

'You're frightened!' He pretended to be surprised.

'Yes, I am! And if you had any sense, you'd be frightened, too!' she said. 'We must get out of here.'

'And where are you going?' he asked politely.

'I'm going home,' she said.

'You mean to Tara?' he said. 'Scarlett, are you mad? The Yankees may be all over Tara by now. You can't go right through the Yankee army!'

'I *will* go home!' she cried, tears running down her cheeks.

Suddenly, she was in his arms. His hands smoothed her hair gently, and when he spoke his voice was gentle, too.

'Don't cry, my brave little girl,' he said. 'I'll take you home.'

♦

Rhett turned west along the narrow street, and the wheel of the wagon hit a stone so hard that Melanie cried out in the back of the wagon. Wade and Prissy were next to her with the new baby. Scarlett was in the front next to Rhett.

'Must we go through the fire?' she asked him.

'Not if we hurry,' he said.

He stopped the horse suddenly. 'Soldiers,' he said.

Long lines of Confederate soldiers walked through Marietta Street, too tired to care about the burning buildings around them. Many had no shoes, and their uniforms were torn and dirty. They went past silently, like ghosts.

'Take a good look,' said Rhett, 'so you can tell your grandchildren that you saw the last soliders of the sacred Cause.'

Suddenly she hated him for insulting these broken men. She thought of Charles, of Ashley who might be dead, and all those brave young boys, now dead. She forgot that she had once thought they were fools.

Rhett watched the soldiers with a strange and thoughtful look on his face. Then there was a crash of falling wood and Scarlett saw a thin flame above the building next to them.

'Rhett, hurry!' she shouted.

They went quickly from one narrow street to another until the sound of the flames died behind them. Rhett did not speak. His face looked cold and hard, as if he'd forgotten where he was. Scarlett wanted him to say something – anything – but he only sat and stared at the dark road ahead.

'Oh, Rhett,' she said. 'I'm so glad you aren't in the army!'

At this, he turned his head – and she saw in his eyes how angry and confused he was. After that, she said nothing.

At last, they were on a wider, smoother road.

'We're out of the city,' said Rhett. 'Do you still want to do this crazy thing? The Yankee army are between you and Tara.'

'Yes!' she said. 'Please, Rhett, let's hurry!'

'You can't go to Jonesboro down this road,' he said, 'they've been fighting up and down there all day. Do you know any wagon paths?'

'Oh, yes,' cried Scarlett. 'I know a wagon path. Pa and I used to ride it. It comes out only a mile from Tara.'

'Good,' said Rhett. 'Maybe the Yankees aren't there yet. Maybe you can get through if –'

'I can get through? Aren't you going to take us?'

'No,' he said. 'I'm leaving you here.'

'Leaving us?' she said wildly. 'Where are you going?'

'I'm going with the army,' he said.

Rhett, stop joking!'

'I'm not joking, my dear,' he said, smiling. 'Think how delighted our soldiers will be at my last-minute appearance.'

'Oh, Rhett!' she cried. 'Why are you going?'

He laughed. 'Perhaps because I'm a Southerner, and I'm ashamed. Who knows?'

'You should *die* of shame, leaving us alone and helpless –'

'Scarlett, anyone as selfish and strong-minded as you is never helpless. God help the Yankees if they get you!' He stepped down from the wagon. Then he put his hands up, caught her under the arms and brought her to the ground next to him. He took her several steps away from the wagon. 'I'm not asking you to understand or forgive,' he said. 'I'll never understand or forgive myself for this foolishness. But the South needs every man, so I'm off to the wars.' His warm, strong hands moved up her arms. 'I do love you, Scarlett, although I told you I didn't. Do you want to change your mind about what I suggested before? A soldier would go to his death with beautiful memories.'

He was kissing her now with slow, hot lips. Charles had never kissed her like this. The kisses of the Tarleton and Calvert boys never made her go hot and cold like this.

A voice came from the wagon. It was Wade's.

'Wade frightened!'

And suddenly Scarlett remembered that she was frightened, too, and that Rhett was leaving her. And on top of it all, he was insulting her with his shocking suggestions!

She pulled herself away from him. 'You coward!' she screamed. 'You nasty, horrible thing!' And she hit him across the mouth with all her strength.

He put a hand to his face. 'I see,' he said quietly.

'Go on!' cried Scarlett. 'I don't want to see you ever again! I hope a shell lands right on you. I hope it blows you into a million pieces. I hope –'

'Never mind the rest,' said Rhett, smiling. 'I understand your general idea.' He walked back to the wagon. 'Mrs Wilkes?'

Prissy's frightened voice answered from the wagon. 'Miss Melanie fainted a long way back, Cap'n Butler.'

'That's probably best,' he said. 'If she was awake, I doubt that she could live through all the pain. Take good care of her, Prissy.' He turned round. 'Goodbye, Scarlett.'

Scarlett knew he was looking at her but she did not speak. She saw his big shoulders moving in the dark, then he was gone. She came slowly back to the wagon, her knees shaking. She put her head against the neck of the horse and cried.

Chapter 10   Home

Many times on that journey Scarlett heard soldiers coming, and had to hide the wagon in fields among the trees; then wait while the men went past like ghosts in the darkness. She lost her way and cried when she could not find the little wagon path she knew so well. But a few miles after she found it, the horse dropped to its knees, too tired to go any further.

Scarlett climbed into the back of the wagon, heard Melanie whisper, 'Scarlett, can I have some water please?' and heard herself answer, 'There isn't any,' before she went to sleep.

When she woke, the sun was pouring through the trees and everything was silent. She sat up and looked round quickly, but there were no soldiers anywhere. In the wagon, Melanie lay so still and white that at first Scarlett thought she must be dead, but then she saw Melanie's shallow breathing.

They were under some trees in someone's front garden, Scarlett noticed. 'It's the Mallory place!' she thought, excited at the thought of friends and help. But the stillness of death lay over the plantation and, when she looked towards the house, there were only some smoke-blackened stones left.

'Is this what Tara will be like?' she thought.

She woke Prissy, then looked over and saw that Melanie's eyes were open.

Scarlett found some apples under the trees, then got some water from a stream near the house. They all had a drink, then Scarlett gave the rest of the water to the horse. The animal was on its feet again but it was very old, she saw now.

They were fifteen miles from Tara, but the horse moved so slowly it took all day to travel there. Every empty, burned-out house they passed frightened Scarlett more. There were dead men and dead horses lying by the road, and the fields and trees seemed full of ghosts in the afternoon sun.

There was a sudden noise and Prissy screamed loudly. But it was only a cow coming from behind some trees. The animal looked at them with large, frightened eyes.

'She needs milkin',' said Prissy.

'It must be one of Mr MacIntosh's that the Yankees didn't get,' said Scarlett. 'We'll take it with us, then we can have some milk for the baby.'

It was evening when they reached the top of a hill and went down through the line of trees that led to Tara. Was it there? Or was the darkness hiding just a few smoke-blackened stones like the MacIntosh place? But no! Tara had escaped! It was there! The white walls showed through the darkness.

Then Scarlett saw a shadow come from inside the house. Someone was home! A shout of delight started in her throat – but died there. The shadow did not move or call to her but, stiffly and slowly, came down the steps.

'Pa?' she whispered. 'It's me, Scarlett. I've come home.'

Her father looked at her. 'Daughter,' he said. 'Daughter.'

'He's an old man!' thought Scarlett, shocked.

A baby's cry came from the wagon and Gerald looked across.

'It's Melanie and her baby,' whispered Scarlett. 'She's very ill – I brought her home.'

Gerald went to the wagon, straightening his shoulders. 'Cousin Melanie!' he said. 'Twelve Oaks is burned. You must stay with us.'

'We must carry her,' said Scarlett. 'She can't walk.'

Another person came from the house. It was Pork, Gerald's personal slave. He ran down the steps. 'Miss Scarlett!'

Scarlett caught him by the arms and felt his tears on her hands as he held them. 'Glad – glad you're back!' he cried.

It was Pork who carried Melanie indoors. Prissy took the baby, Wade followed them up the steps into the house. Scarlett caught her father's arm before he could follow, too.

'Did they get well, Pa?' she said.

'The girls are getting better,' he said. 'Your mother –'

'Yes?'

'Your mother died yesterday,' said Gerald.

♦

Gerald said it over and over again as he followed Scarlett around the house. 'She died yesterday – she died yesterday.' Scarlett felt nothing except a great tiredness. She would think of Mother later, or she would simply cry and cry.

Later, when she was alone with her father, she asked, 'Why didn't the Yankees burn Tara?'

'They used the house for offices,' said Gerald.

'Yankees – in this house?' The thought made her feel sick.

'They were, daughter,' said Gerald. 'We saw the smoke from Twelve Oaks before they came. But Miss Honey and Miss India were in Macon, so we didn't worry about them. We couldn't go to Macon. The girls were so sick – your mother – we couldn't go. Our negroes ran away. They stole the wagons and the horses. Only Mammy, Dilcey and Pork stayed. The Yankees came up the road from the river and I met them at the front door.'

'Oh, brave little Gerald!' thought Scarlett.

'They told me to leave,' went on Gerald. 'They told me they were going to burn the place. I told them that we had typhoid in the house and they would burn it over the heads of three dying women. The young officer was – was a gentleman.'

'A Yankee gentleman? Pa!'

'A gentleman,' said Gerald. 'He rode away and came back with an army doctor who looked at the girls – and your mother.'

'You let a Yankee into their room?'

'He had medicine and we had none. He saved your sisters,' said Gerald. 'They didn't burn the house, they moved in. The officers filled all the rooms except the sick room, and the soldiers lived in tents around the place. They killed the cows, the chickens and the pigs. They took the pictures and some of the furniture.'

'And – and Mother? Did she know Yankees were in the house?'

'She never knew anything.'

'Thank God,' said Scarlett.

'And then they moved on.' He was silent for a long time and then he held her hand. 'I'm glad you're home,' he said simply.

♦

After Gerald went to bed, Scarlett went to the room where Careen and Suellen were sleeping. Mammy was there, watching them. Her eyes lit up when she saw Scarlett.

'My child is home!' Mammy said softly. 'Oh, Miss Scarlett, now that Miss Ellen is dead, what are we goin' to do?'

Scarlett sat down next to the bed. 'I want you to tell me about Mother,' she said, 'I just couldn't ask Pa about her.'

Tears came from Mammy's eyes. 'It was those Slattery trash that killed Miss Ellen. I told her an' told her not to –'

'Slatterys?' said Scarlett, confused.

'Emmie Slattery was sick with typhoid an' Miss Ellen went to nurse her,' said Mammy. 'I told her to leave those white trash alone, but she didn' listen. Then, when Emmie was gettin' better, Miss Careen went down with typhoid, an' then Miss Suellen. So Miss Ellen had to nurse them, too. With all the fightin' up the road, an' the Yankees across the river, an' the field negroes runnin' off every night, I was nearly crazy with worry. But Miss Ellen was cool an' calm, except that she worried because we couldn't get medicines. An' then she went down with typhoid, too.' Mammy dried her tears before she went on. 'Miss Ellen went fast, Miss Scarlett. Even that nice Yankee doctor couldn't do anythin' for her. She died a few nights after the cotton burned –'

'Has the cotton gone?' said Scarlett. 'Tell me!'

'Yes, Miss Scarlett. The Yankees burned it.'

'Three years' cotton!' thought Scarlett. 'One hundred and fifty thousand dollars, in one big fire!'

Chapter 11   Murder

Next morning, when Scarlett went down to breakfast, Gerald was sitting at the table. As Scarlett sat down, he said, 'We will wait for Mrs O'Hara. She is late.'

Scarlett stared at him. He was looking at her in a strange and confused way, and his hands were shaking.

'Has Pa lost his mind?' thought Scarlett. 'No! He'll get better. He *must* get better! I won't think about it now. I won't think of him or Mother or any of these awful things!'

She left the room without eating.

Pork was outside the house. 'Have you been over to Twelve Oaks or the MacIntosh place to see if there's anything left in the gardens that we can eat?' Scarlett asked him.

'No, Miss,' said Pork, 'We ain't left Tara.'

'You go to MacIntosh, and I'll go to Twelve Oaks,' she said.

The road was hot and dusty, but she was hungry, and they needed food from somewhere. At the bottom of the hill was the river, and Scarlett took off her shoes and put her feet into the cool water before going on to Twelve Oaks.

It was burned down, and just a few blackened stones were left of the house where she had danced and flirted with the men, and dreamed her dreams of marrying Ashley.

'Oh, Ashley, I hope you are dead!' she thought. 'I don't want you to see this!'

She walked to the garden and found some potatoes in the soft earth. Without stopping to clean it, Scarlett picked up a potato and began to eat. But it was old and the taste was bitter, and Scarlett was sick almost immediately.

Then she lay down, her face against the earth, and thought of the people who were dead, the way of life that had gone forever, and the dark and frightening future.

But the past was the past, Scarlett told herself, sitting up. Those lazy, happy old days were gone, never to return. There was no going back. 'I'm going to live through this,' she said aloud. 'And when it's over, I'm never going to be hungry again. If I have to steal or kill – as God is my witness – I'm never going to be hungry again!'

♦

After two weeks, she knew that her father would never get any better. He would always be waiting for Ellen, always listening for her. When Scarlett asked him for advice, his only answer was, 'Do what you think best, daughter.'

One morning, she was at the open window of her bedroom. She had hurt her foot and was sitting in a chair. Melanie was in her room with the children, Careen and Suellen were in their room, and Gerald, Mammy, Pork and Dilcey were in the fields.

Scarlett was wondering how they were going to buy food. The only money in the house was Confederate money, and that had almost no value now. 'And if I can get my hands on some money,' she thought, 'how can we carry food from Jonesboro to Tara?' The old horse that brought them from Atlanta had died.

It was while she was worrying that she heard the sound of a horse. She looked up quickly – *and saw a Yankee soldier*. He was a rough-looking man with an untidy black beard – and a gun! And he was getting off his horse outside the front door.

Scarlett heard him come into the house and walk through the rooms downstairs. 'In a moment,' she thought, 'he'll walk into the kitchen!' There, cooking over the fire in two large pots, were apples and vegetables – brought painfully from Twelve Oaks and the MacIntosh garden – dinner for nine hungry people, but only really enough for two. The thought of the Yankee eating their meal made Scarlett so angry that she began to shake.

She went to the cupboard and took out the heavy gun which Charles had never used. Then, quickly and silently, she ran downstairs, holding it behind her.

'Who's there?' he shouted. And she stopped in the middle of the stairs. He was standing in the doorway of the dining-room, his gun in one hand. 'So there is somebody home,' he said, smiling and putting his gun away. He walked across

He was standing in the doorway of the dining-room, his gun in one hand. 'So there is somebody home,' he said.

until he was standing below her. 'All alone, little lady?' he said.

Before he could move again, Scarlett lifted her gun and shot him in the face. The noise filled her ears and the man crashed backwards on to the floor. Scarlett ran down and stood over him, looking into what was left of his face. As she looked, two streams of blood ran across the floor, one from his face and one from the back of his head. He was dead. She had killed a man. 'Murder,' she thought. 'I've done murder. Oh, this can't be happening to me!'

A sound behind her made Scarlett turn round. Melanie, wearing only a night-dress, was coming down the stairs. She saw the dead Yankee, then smiled proudly at Scarlett.

'She – she's like me!' thought Scarlett. 'She would do the same thing!'

'Scarlett! Scarlett!' cried the frightened voices of her sisters. Then Wade began to scream. Melanie climbed back up the stairs and opened the door of the girls' room.

'Don't be frightened!' she said, laughing. 'Your sister was trying to clean Charles' gun, and it went off and nearly frightened her to death! Wade, your mother just shot your dear Pa's gun. When you get older, she'll let you shoot it, too.'

'What a cool liar!' thought Scarlett. 'I couldn't think that quickly. But why did she lie? They've got to know I've done it.'

Melanie came back downstairs, although she was weak and in pain. 'Scarlett, we must get him out of here,' she said. 'He may not be alone, and if more soldiers come and find him –'

'He must be alone,' said Scarlett. 'I didn't see any others from the upstairs window.'

'Well, no one must know about it,' said Melanie. 'The negroes might talk and then they'll come and get you. We must hide him before they come back.'

'I could dig a hole in the corner of the garden and put him in it,' said Scarlett. 'But how will I get him there?'

'We'll each take a leg and pull him,' said Melanie.

'You couldn't pull a cat. You'll kill yourself.'

'All right,' said Melanie. 'You pull him out and I'll clean up the mess. But can't we go through his bag and his pockets first? He might have something to eat.'

Scarlett found a wallet inside his coat. It was full of money – United States money as well as Confederate money, and one ten-dollar gold coin and two five-dollar gold coins. Melanie found some coffee in the bag, and there were rings and other small pieces of jewellery in his pockets.

'A thief!' whispered Melanie. 'He stole all this! I'm glad you killed him, Scarlett.'

♦

No one asked where the horse came from, they were just pleased to have him. The Yankee lay covered in the hole in the corner of the garden. No ghost came to frighten Scarlett during the long nights when she lay awake afterwards.

'I won't think about it,' she said to herself.

But whenever she had to do something difficult after this, she thought: 'I've done murder, so I can do this.'

Chapter 12   Peace, At Last

By May, 1865, the war was over and the Confederacy had lost. The dream they had loved and hoped for, the Cause which took the lives of their friends, was finished. But Scarlett cried no tears. She simply thought: 'Thank God! Now the cow won't be stolen. Now the horse is safe. Now I won't be afraid to drive round the country looking for something to eat. And if Ashley is alive, he'll be coming home.'

In that warm summer after peace came, a stream of Confederate soldiers came through Tara, on their way home. Most were walking, although a few lucky ones had a horse. They asked each soldier for news of Ashley, and Suellen asked about Mr Kennedy, but none of them knew anything.

Then, one afternoon, Uncle Peter surprised them all by arriving from Atlanta. He came on an old horse and brought news of Aunt Pitty, who wanted Melanie and Scarlett to come back to live with her again.

He also brought a letter – from Ashley.

'He's comin' home!' Uncle Peter told them. 'He's alive!'

Melanie fainted, but Scarlett took the letter and opened it quickly. She recognized Ashley's writing:

My love, I am coming home to you –

Tears filled her eyes so that she could not read any more. Holding the letter, she ran to her mother's room while the others tried to help Melanie. She shut the door, then crying and laughing and kissing the letter, she whispered, 'My love, I am coming home to you!'

◆

When weeks went by and Ashley did not come, Scarlett began to worry that something had happened to him along the way.

The never-ending line of soldiers went through, and Scarlett's heart began to grow hard. They were eating the food which was meant for the mouths of Tara. Food was hard to get, and the money in the Yankee's wallet would not last forever.

Will Benteen was a soldier who was very ill when he arrived. One of his legs finished at the knee, and a roughly cut wooden leg was fitted to it. He looked like a poor farmer, not a plantation owner, but this did not stop the girls working to save his life. Then, one day, he opened his light blue eyes and saw Careen sitting beside him.

'Then you weren't a dream, after all,' he said.

Will had owned a small farm in Georgia, and two negroes. He knew that his slaves were free now, and that his farm was burned, but these things did not seem to worry him.

'You've been good to me, Miss Scarlett,' he said. 'And, if you'll let me, I'm goin' to stay here and help you with all the work until I've paid you back. I can't ever pay it all, because there's no price a man can pay for his life.'

So he stayed and, slowly and quietly, a large part of the work and worry of Tara, passed from Scarlett to him.

♦

It was a warm September afternoon, and Will was sitting on the front steps of Tara, talking to Scarlett. Melanie came out to join them. Although she did her share of the work at Tara, she was thin and never completely well.

Will was talking about his trip to Fayetteville that morning when he looked along the road leading to Tara.

'Another soldier,' he said.

Scarlett looked and saw a man with a beard, wearing the usual grey and blue uniform which was dusty and torn.

'I hope he isn't very hungry,' she said.

'He'll be hungry,' said Will.

Melanie stood up. 'I'll tell Dilcey to —'

She stopped so suddenly that Scarlett turned to look at her. Melanie's hand was at her throat and her face was white. 'She's going to faint,' thought Scarlett, jumping to her feet.

But Melanie was running down the steps, her arms stretching out towards the soldier. And then Scarlett knew the truth.

The man lifted his face and looked towards the house, as if he was too tired to take another step. Melanie, crying out, threw herself into his arms.

Scarlett took two steps forward, but Will stopped her.

'Don't spoil it,' he said quietly.

'Let me go, you fool! Let me go! It's Ashley!'

Will held her. 'He's her husband, ain't he?' he said calmly.

Scarlett looked at him angrily — and in the quiet kindness of his eyes she saw understanding and pity.

ACTIVITIES

Chapters 1–2

Before you read

1 Look at the Word List at the back of the book.
  a Which of these words can be used when talking about
    women?
    charm   flirt   Pa   prostitute   wagon   widow
  b Which of these words are for feelings?
    delighted   disappointed   sacred   content
2 Read the Introduction and answer these questions. What do you
  know about:
  a Scarlett O'Hara?
  b Ashley Wilkes?
  c Rhett Butler?
  d The southern states of the US in 1861?

While you read

3 Match these names with the descriptions.
  Scarlett O'Hara   Stuart and Brent Tarleton
  Gerald O'Hara   Ellen O'Hara   Pittypat Hamilton
  Ashley Wilkes   Mammy   Charlie Hamilton
  a Charles and Melanie's aunt who lives
    in Atlanta   ....
  b twins who want to dance with Scarlett
    at the party   ....
  c an old negro woman who works for the
    O'Hara family   ....
  d a sixteen-year-old girl in love with Ashley
    Wilkes   ....
  e Melanie Hamilton's brother   ....
  f the owner of a plantation in Georgia
    called Tara   ....
  g the man who is going to marry Melanie
    Hamilton   ....

h Gerald's wife who is always nursing sick
  negroes and 'white trash'   ....

4 Write the name of the person from the story. Who:

  a loves Brent Tarleton?   ....

  b is the father of Honey and India?   ....

  c shot a man in Charleston?   ....

After you read

5 How does Gerald O'Hara feel about these? Why?

  a Tara

  b the Wilkes family

  c the Slatterys

6 How does the relationship between these people change? Why?

  a Ellen O'Hara and Jonas Wilkerson

  b Scarlett O'Hara and Charles Hamilton

Chapters 3–4

Before you read

7 What kind of person is Scarlett? How does she behave with
men? Do you think Ashley will marry her instead of Melanie?

8 In what ways will the start of war change Scarlett's life, do you
think?

While you read

9 Are these sentences true (T) or false (F)?

  a Gerald O'Hara wants to fight the Yankees but
  John Wilkes wants peace.   .....

  b Rhett Butler's opinion of the Yankees' greater
  strength shocks everyone.   .....

  c Scarlett first tells Ashley of her love for him and
  then says she hates him.   .....

  d When Rhett Butler gets up off the sofa, Scarlett
  almost faints from shock and embarrassment.   .....

  e When Scarlett says Rhett is not a gentleman,
  he tells her she is not a lady.   .....

   f India Wilkes is annoyed with Scarlett for flirting
    with Charles and she tells Melanie about Scarlett's
    love for Ashley.   .....

   g Scarlett marries Charles because he has money
    and she wants to hurt Honey, Ashley and Melanie.   .....

   h After Charles dies of typhoid, Scarlett has a son,
    Wade.   .....

10 Circle the correct word in *italics* in each sentence.

   a Belle Watling is a *nurse/prostitute* in Atlanta.

   b Melanie and Aunt Pitty go to the sale to help the *McLures/Cause*.

   c Captain Butler is a blockade runner who brings things to *Atlanta/Charleston* and sells them.

   d Dr Meade tries to stop Rhett Butler from dancing with Scarlett because she is a *widow/mother*.

   e Scarlett tells Melanie that Captain Butler runs the blockade for money and does not care about the *Yankees/Confederacy*.

After you read

11 Discuss the difference between:

   a Ashley Wilkes and Rhett Butler.

   b Scarlett and Melanie.

12 Work with another student. Have this conversation.

   Student A: You are Aunt Pittypat. It is the day after the dance. You are shocked that Scarlett danced with Captain Butler. Discuss this with Melanie.

   Student B: You are Melanie. Give Aunt Pittypat your opinion of Scarlett's behaviour. Try to calm your aunt's fears. Explain how life is different during a war.

Chapters 5–6

Before you read

13 Read the titles of Chapters 5 and 6 and answer these questions. Who do you think:

   a will be a hero? Why?

   b will be missing?

14 Put these events in the correct order. Write 1–8.

   a Scarlett sees the names of Brent, Stuart and
       Thomas Tarleton on the list of the dead.   .....

   b News comes that Dr and Mrs Meade's son
       Darcy has been killed at the battle of Gettysburg
       but Ashley is alive.   .....

   c Captain Butler says all wars as sacred to the
       people who start them.   .....

   d Rhett tells Scarlett that the war is not about the
       negroes.   .....

   e Melanie shocks Mrs Merriwether by saying that
       Ashley's letters are about the uselessness of war.   .....

   f Rhett Butler upsets the older men and women in
       Atlanta with his talk of 'the brave boys' and 'our
       heroes in grey'.   .....

   g After Ashley comes home for a week, Melanie is
       expecting their first child.   .....

   h Captain Butler brings news that Ashley is alive.   .....

After you read

15 Discuss with another student. What does:

   a Scarlett think about her visits to Tara? Why?
   b Mrs Merriwether think of Rhett Butler's ideas about the war?
   c Scarlett think about Ashley and Rhett's opinions of the war?
   d the battle at Gettysburg mean to the Confederacy?
   e Ashley feel for Scarlett, do you think?

16 What is your opinion of Rhett Butler? Why?

Chapters 7–8

Before you read

17 Read the titles of Chapters 7 and 8 and look at the picture on page 39. What do you think will happen?

18 Do you think Scarlett will fall in love with Rhett? Why (not)?

19 Circle the correct answer: 1, 2 or 3.

    a What happens when the Yankees come close to Atlanta?

        1) Scarlett and Melanie take Prissy and Wade to Tara.

        2) Scarlett hears from Tara that her sister Careen has typhoid.

        3) Rhett tells Scarlett that he loves her and wants to marry her.

    b Why can't Dr and Mrs Meade go to Melanie's bedside?

        1) Mrs Meade gets a message that her son Phil is coming home.

        2) They are at the railway station trying to leave the city.

        3) Their son has been shot, and other soldiers need the doctor.

    c During childbirth, Melanie starts calling Ashley's name, and Scarlett wants to

        1) cover Melanie's face with a pillow.

        2) tell Melanie that Phil Meade is hurt.

        3) leave Melanie and her baby for the Yankees.

After you read

20 Who says this and why?

    a 'With these shells falling, it may be at any time.'

    b 'You mean because she's Ashley Wilkes' widow.'

    c 'Are you asking me to marry you?'

    d 'You could be at home if it weren't for me, couldn't you?'

    e 'I was lyin', Miss Scarlett!'

Chapters 9–10

Before you read

21 What do you think will happen to Melanie and her baby?

22 Read the title of Chapters 9 and 10. Who do you think escapes from Atlanta? Where is home, do you think?

23 Write the missing word(s) in these sentences.

    a Rhett finds a .... to take Scarlett, Wade, Prissy, Melanie and her baby son to Tara.

    b When Rhett sees the Confederate soldiers, he says they are the last soldiers of the .... Cause.

    c Rhett leaves Scarlett because he has decided to fight in the Confederate ....

    d When Rhett suggests they become lovers, she .... him in the mouth.

    e There is nothing except smoke-blackened stones on the Mallory's .... near Tara.

    f When Scarlett arrives at Tara, her father is like an old man and her mother is ....

    g Gerald is grateful to the .... because their doctor saved his daughters and they didn't burn the house.

    h The Yankees burned the O'Hara's ...., which had a value of a hundred and fifty thousand dollars.

After you read

24 Who does these things and why?

    a burns the gun factory

    b dresses in a white coat and trousers with pockets full of bullets

    c cries because she can not find the right wagon path

    d moves into Tara and uses it for offices

    e nurses Emmie Slattery when she is sick with typhoid

25 Discuss Captain Butler's reasons for deciding to fight in the war.

Chapters 11–12

Before you read

26 Read the titles of Chapters 11 and 12. Who will murder who, do you think? Why?

27 Although Tara has been saved, the family have lost Ellen, their cotton and their horses. Their confederate money has almost no value. How will they feed themselves, do you think?

While you read

28 Answer these questions. Write *Yes* or *No*.

    a Has Gerald lost his mind? .....

    b Does Scarlett go to Twelve Oaks to find Ashley? .....

    c Does Scarlett think she will steal or kill for food if she has to? .....

    d Are there enough apples and vegetables to easily feed nine hungry people? .....

    e Does Scarlett kill the Yankee soldier? .....

    f Does Melanie suggest that they should steal from the dead man's pockets and hide his body? .....

    g After killing the soldier, is Scarlett frightened? .....

29 Put these events in the correct order. Write a–f.

    1 .....   2 .....   3 .....   4 .....   5 .....   6 .....

    a Confederate soldiers stop and eat at Tara, which annoys Scarlett.

    b Melanie recognizes Ashley before Scarlett does.

    c When Scarlett sees another Confederate soldier in his dusty and torn uniform, she hopes he doesn't want food.

    d After the O'Hara women save Will Benteen's life, he stays at Tara to help them.

    e Uncle Peter arrives from Atlanta with news of Aunt Pitty and a letter from Ashley.

    f Will does not allow Scarlett to ruin Melanie and Ashley's emotional meeting but he feels pity for Scarlett.

After you read

30 What does Scarlett think after:

    a leaving Gerald at the table?

    b seeing Twelve Oaks?

    c eating a bad potato?

    d killing the soldier?

    e hearing Melanie lie to Wade and her sisters?

    f the Confederacy loses the war?

31 What hope is there now for:

    a the South?

    b Scarlett?

    c Melanie and Ashley?

    d Gerald O'Hara?

    e Will Benteen?

Writing

32 Imagine that you are Scarlett and it is the night before the party at Twelve Oaks. Write what Scarlett puts in her diary that night about her plans for the party.

33 Imagine you are Ashley and you are writing a letter to Melanie. You are a prisoner now and you have seen many men die. Tell Melanie your opinion of the war. Try to make her understand that you are not a coward.

34 Write a report on the deaths of Dr Meade's son, Darcy, and the three sons of the Tarletons for the Atlanta newspaper.

35 Write the letter from Scarlett that Prissy took to Dr Meade about Melanie's baby.

36 Rhett Butler wants Scarlett to be his lover. In what ways are Scarlett and Rhett similar? Write a comparison of these two characters. What will happen between them in Part 2, do you think? Explain.

37 Imagine you are Suellen O'Hara. Your mother is dead and Scarlett is back at Tara with Wade, Melanie and her baby. Write a letter to a cousin who also lives in the south and tell him or her about the Yankees at Tara during the war.

38 Would you like Scarlett for a friend? Make a list of your reasons for liking or not liking her.

39 War changes people in different ways. Do you agree or disagree? Write your opinion.

40 After the war ended, the negroes were free. Do you think that Mammy, Pork and Prissy will leave the O'Hara's? Why (not)? Write what you think will happen to them in Part 2.

41 What should Melanie and Ashley do now that they are together again with their son. Write a letter to them and give them some advice.

WORD LIST

automatically (adv) without thinking about what you are doing

battle (n) a fight between two armies or large groups

blockade (n) a situation in which soldiers let nothing and nobody enter or leave a place

burst (v) to break open suddenly because of being very full

carriage (n) a vehicle pulled by a horse, used for carrying people

charm (v/n) to behave in an attractive way that makes people like you; someone who pleases people easily has **charm**

cheek (n) the soft round part of your face below your eye

content (adj) happy and satisfied

delighted (adj) very pleased; this feeling is **delight**

disappointed (adj) unhappy because something you hoped for did not happen or was not very good

flirt (v) to show someone playfully that you think he/she is attractive

forever (adv) for always

laughter (n) the act of laughing, or the sound of laughing

Mammy (n) an old name for an African-American woman who looked after other people's children

negro (n) an old word for a black person

Pa (n) Father

pray (v) to speak to God

prostitute (n) someone who earns money by having sex

relation (n) a member of your family

row (n) a line of people or things that are next to each other

rumour (n) information that people tell each other, but that they are not sure is true

sacred (adj) important and special according to the ideas of a religion

shell (n) a large bullet that is shot from a big gun and causes an explosion when it hits something

slave (n) someone who belongs to another person and must work for them without any pay

snake-in-the-grass (n) a dishonest person

suspect (v) to think that someone may be guilty of doing something bad

trash (n) a word meaning 'rubbish' and used rudely to describe people from a low social class

typhoid (n) a serious disease caused by dirty food or drink, that spreads easily from person to person

wagon (n) a strong vehicle for carrying things, usually pulled by a horse

widow (n) a woman whose husband has died

Gone with the Wind – Part Two
Margaret Mitchell

Gone with the Wind is a great romantic story of love and war and one of the best-selling books of all time. In Part 2, the American Civil War has destroyed Scarlett O'Hara's comfortable world. Will she lose her home too? Or can she save it and rebuild her life?

Emma
Jane Austen

Emma Woodhouse is beautiful, clever and rich. She likes to arrange marriages between her friends and neighbours in the village of Highbury. But Emma makes a lot of mistakes and causes more problems than happy marriages. Then she almost loses her own chance of love.

Love Actually
Richard Curtis

In London, Christmas is coming and the people in this story have love on their minds. Some have found love; some have lost it. Some accept their loneliness; others live in hope. Even the new British prime minister's thoughts are not always on his job – because love, actually, is all around us.

There are hundreds of Penguin Readers to choose from – world classics, film adaptations, modern-day crime and adventure, short stories, biographies, American classics, non-fiction, plays ...

For a complete list of all Penguin Readers titles, please contact your local Pearson Longman office or visit our website.

Longman Dictionaries

Express yourself with confidence!

*Longman has led the way in ELT dictionaries since 1935.
We constantly talk to students and teachers around the
world to find out what they need from a learner's dictionary.*

Why choose a Longman dictionary?

Easy to understand

Longman invented the Defining Vocabulary – 2000 of the most
common words which are used to write the definitions in our
dictionaries. So Longman definitions are always clear and easy
to understand.

Real, natural English

All Longman dictionaries contain natural examples taken from
real-life that help explain the meaning of a word and show you
how to use it in context.

Avoid common mistakes

Longman dictionaries are written specially for learners, and we
make sure that you get all the help you need to avoid common
mistakes. We analyse typical learners' mistakes and include
notes on how to avoid them.

Innovative CD-ROMs

Longman are leaders in dictionary CD-ROM innovation. Did
you know that a dictionary CD-ROM includes features to help
improve your pronunciation, help you practice for exams and
improve your writing skills?

**For details of all Longman dictionaries, and to choose
the one that's right for you, visit our website:**

www.longman.com/dictionaries